French sticker book

Dominique Debney

Illustrated by Sascha Lipscomb

Note to Parents

A foreign language is part of every child's school curriculum and an important skill for modern life. It is never too early to start learning French, but parents need to make sure that a child's first experiences of another language are positive and enjoyable.

This **French Sticker Book** is designed to make learning French fun. It introduces everyday words and phrases through a series of scenes featuring a lively group of friends. Each scene is accompanied by a sticker activity, which provides a simple and satisfying way to practise the language they have just learned.

Each double page is based on a particular theme, such as pets, numbers or food and drink. At the centre of the book are four pages of colour stickers, grouped according to their theme. Your child will enjoy using his or her new knowledge of French to choose the right stickers to fill the gaps on the page. For example, he or she will soon work out that the sticker showing a birthday cake with five candles belongs to the child saying *J'ai cinq ans* (I am five).

There is a vocabulary at the end of the book, giving the meaning of all words and phrases which appear on each double page. It also includes a pronunciation guide.

How to help your child:

* Look through the book together and make sure your child understands how the sticker activities work.

* Give assistance where necessary, but let your child work at his or her own pace.

* Try to introduce French into your daily lives. Start by saying *Bonjour* first thing in the morning, and *Merci* instead of *Thank you*, and gradually introduce more words and phrases. This is an easy way to build your child's confidence in speaking another language.

* Don't worry if you do not speak French yourself. You and your child can learn together! Make sure you refer to the pronunciation guide at the back of the book.

Bonne chance! (Good luck!)

Comment tu t'appelles?

Francine has invited some friends to a fancy dress party. Look at the stickers carefully. Can you work out who's who?

Place the stickers under the correct speech bubbles.

Une journée typique

What are these people saying?

Find the right stickers to put in the speech bubbles.

Combien?

1 un  nounours

2 deux  livres

3 trois  ballons

4 quatre  glaces

5 cinq  gâteaux

6 six  fraises

7 sept  bougies

8 huit  clés

9 neuf  citrons

10 dix  bonbons

Find the stickers to go with these labels.

| dix fraises | deux nounours | huit clés |

| six glaces | neuf bougies | quatre gâteaux |

Use your calculator to learn how the things below are written in French.

Press the keys shown, turn the calculator upside down and read the words. Then complete the words below by writing in the missing letters.

You add it to your chips.

| sept | trois | cinq |

D U _ _ _

Something bright and warm.

| sept | un | trois | sept | zéro | cinq |

L E _ _ **L** _ _ **L**

Bon anniversaire!

All these children have a birthday today. Can you give them their correct balloon, card or cake?

Qu'est-ce que c'est?

Join the dots to discover what various animals are called in French.

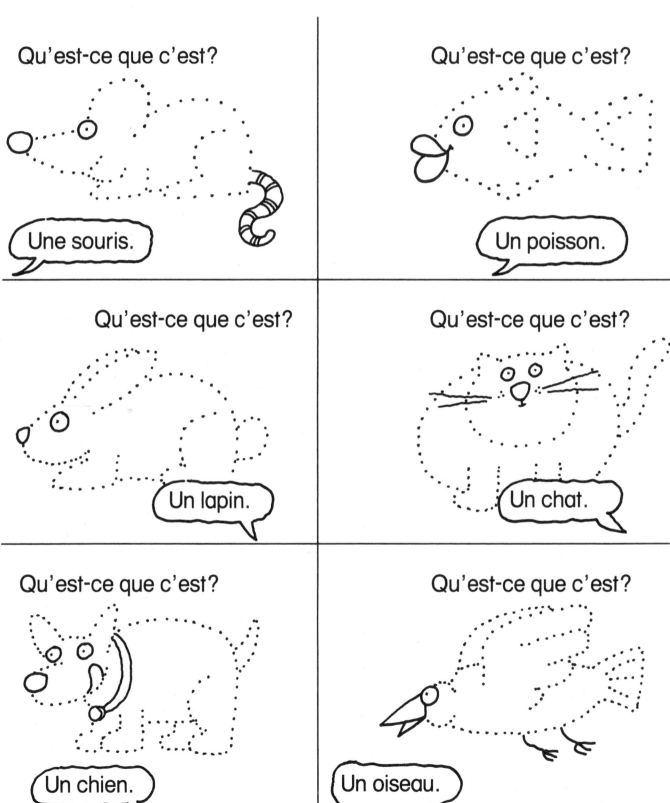

The children are saying what pets they have got and showing us photos of them. Find the correct stickers to go into each frame.

Les frères et sœurs

Les frères et sœurs

Qu'est-ce qu'on porte?

Les contraires

Je compte jusqu'à 20

Comment tu t'appelles?

Une journée typique

Salut!

Salut!

Bonjour Monsieur.

**Au revoir.
Bon voyage!**

**Bonjour
les enfants.**

**Bonjour
Madame.**

**Bonne nuit
les enfants.**

Combien?

 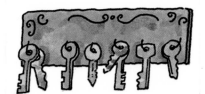 

Bon anniversaire!

Qu'est-ce que c'est?

Je compte jusqu'à 20

Bon appétit!

Les préférences

The children are telling us about their brothers and sisters and showing us their photos. Can you find the stickers to fill in the frames?

Qu'est-ce qu'on porte?

Francine porte

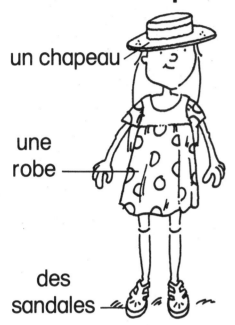

un chapeau

une
robe

des
sandales

Antoine porte

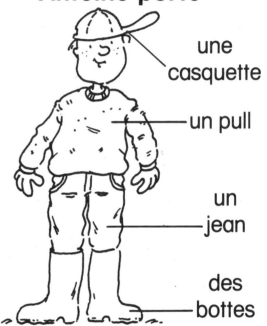

une
casquette

un pull

un
jean

des
bottes

Karim porte

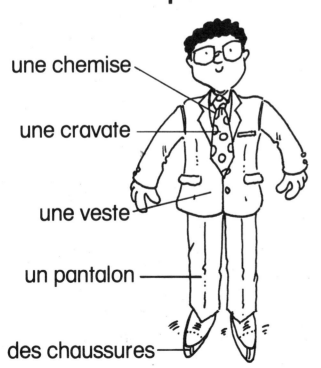

une chemise

une cravate

une veste

un pantalon

des chaussures

Colette porte

un tee-shirt

une jupe

des chaussettes

des
baskets

Who is speaking? Find out by reading the speech balloons and then choosing the sticker showing the person who is wearing the right clothes.

Les contraires

What are they talking about? Find out by selecting the correct stickers.

Link the opposites using a different colour pencil each time, then
colour the two boxes in the same colour. One has been done for you.

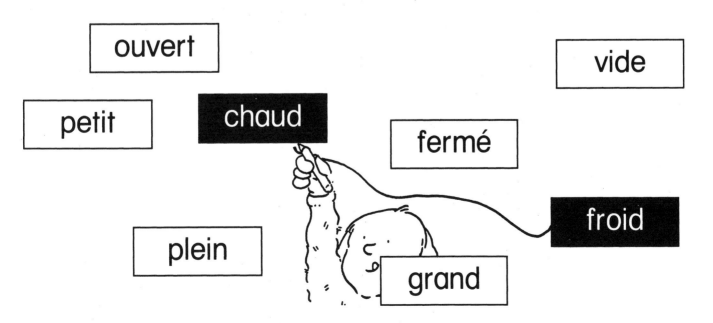

Je compte jusqu'à 20

11	12	13	14	15
onze	douze	treize	quatorze	quinze
16	17	18	19	20
seize	dix-sept	dix-huit	dix-neuf	vingt

Find the stickers with the correct totals.

douze

quinze

vingt

dix-huit

onze

Here are some objects from Francine's house. Measure them with a ruler. Then fill in the missing letters to complete each sentence.

La montre mesure d _ _ - n _ _ _ centimètres.

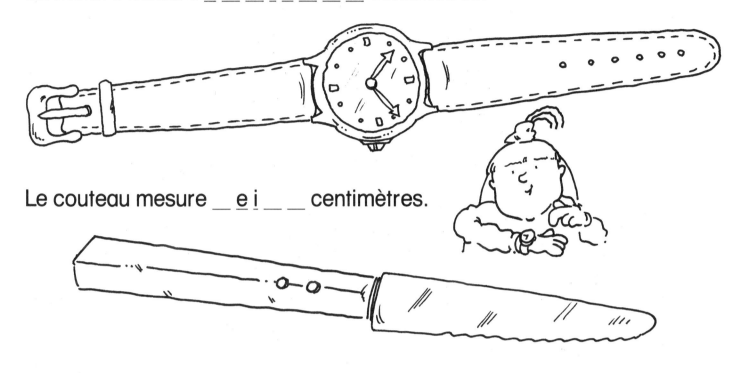

Le couteau mesure _ e i _ _ centimètres.

La brosse à dents mesure _ i _ - _ _ p t centimètres.

La cuiller mesure q _ _ t _ _ _ _ centimètres.

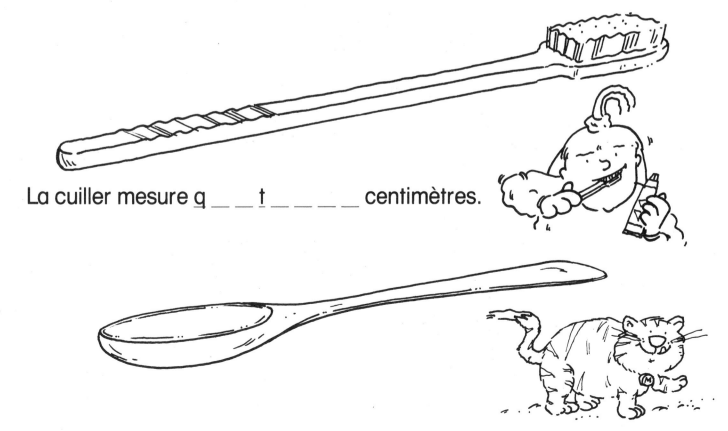

Bon appétit!

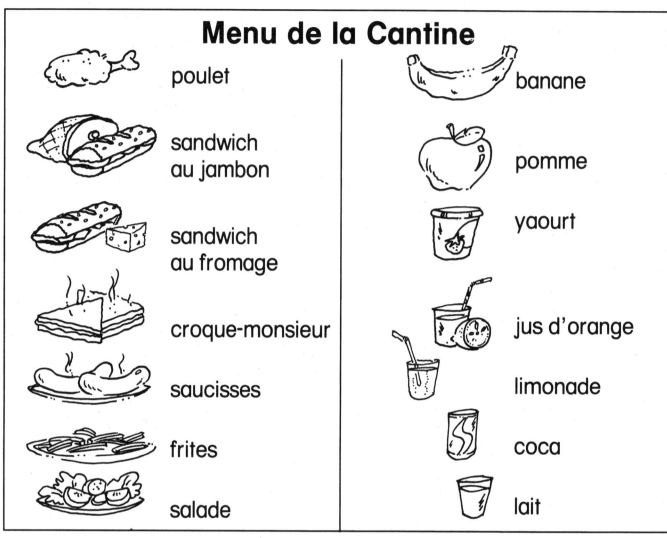

Menu de la Cantine

poulet

sandwich au jambon

sandwich au fromage

croque-monsieur

saucisses

frites

salade

banane

pomme

yaourt

jus d'orange

limonade

coca

lait

Je mange une pomme.

Je bois un jus d'orange.

Je mange un croque-monsieur.

Je bois du lait.

The children are ordering things to eat and drink. Find the correct trays and stick them on the table in front of the right person.

Un sandwich au fromage, une banane et un jus d'orange, s'il vous plaît.

Des saucisses, des frites et une limonade, s'il vous plaît.

Un croque-monsieur, des frites, une pomme et un coca, s'il vous plaît.

Du poulet, de la salade et du lait, s'il vous plaît.

An extra tray has been set aside for you. Stick it in and say in French what you will eat and drink. Is there anything else you would like from the menu?

Les préférences

First, find the missing pictures and stick them in the correct boxes.
Then, look at all the things on the page and say whether you like them
or not. Start with **J'aime** or **Je n'aime pas**.

faire ma
toilette

la neige

la pluie

chanter

jouer au
football

faire la
vaisselle

l'école

lire

les
araignées

la peinture

VOCABULAIRE *[vo-ka-bew-lair]* VOCABULARY

For convenience, the vocabulary is listed under each topic.

All the French words and phrases are followed by a guide to the way they sound. The pronunciation guide appears in italics. You can simply read the words as you would English words, providing that you follow these rules:

Pronounce the 'a' as in **apple**, the 'j' as the 's' in **treasure**. Do not sound the '(r)' or '(g)'; they are only there to ensure the correct pronunciation of the sounds which come before.

Of course, if you can enlist the help of someone who speaks French, all the better!

COMMENT TU T'APPELLES? *[ko-mon-(g)-tew-ta-pell]* WHAT IS YOUR NAME?
Je m'appelle... *[je(r)-ma-pell]* My name is...
Et toi? *[ay-twa]* And you?

UNE JOURNEE TYPIQUE *[ewn-joor-nay-tee-peek]* A TYPICAL DAY
départ *[day-par]* start, departure
arrivée *[ar-ree-vay]* finish, arrival
bonjour *[bon(g)-joor]* hello, good morning
Maman *[ma-mon(g)]* Mummy
Papa *[pa-pa]* Daddy
au revoir *[or-vwar]* goodbye
Bonne journée *[bonn-joor-nay]* Have a nice day!
Monsieur l'agent *[me(r)-sye(r)-la-jon(g)]* Constable
Salut! *[sa-lew]* Hi!
les enfants *[lay-zon(g)-fon(g)]* (the) children
Mademoiselle *[mad-mwa-zell]* Miss
bonne nuit *[bonn-nwee]* good night
bon voyage *[bon(g)-vwa-yaj]* have a nice journey
école *[ay-kol]* school

COMBIEN? *[kon(g)-bee-an(g)]* HOW MUCH, HOW MANY?
1 *[un(g)]*, **2** *[de(r)]*, **3** *[trwa]*, **4** *[ka-tre(r)]*, **5** *[san(g)k]*, **6** *[seess]*, **7** *[set]*, **8** *[weet]*, **9** *[ne(r)f]*, **10** *[deess]*,

un nounours *[un(g)-noo-noorss]* a/one teddy
deux livres *[de(r)-leevr]* two books
trois ballons *[trwa-ba-lon(g)]* three balls
quatre glaces *[ka-tre(r)-glass]* four ice-creams
cinq gâteaux *[san(g)-ga-toe]* five cakes
six fraises *[see-frayz]* six strawberries
sept bougies *[set-boo-jee]* seven candles
huit clés *[wee-klay]* eight keys
neuf citrons *[ne(r)f-see-tron(g)]* nine lemons
dix bonbons *[dee-bon(g)-bon(g)]* ten sweets
le soleil *[le(r)-so-laye(r)]* the sun
du sel *[dew-sell]* some salt

BON ANNIVERSAIRE! *[bonn-a-nee-vair-sair]* HAPPY BIRTHDAY!
Joyeux anniversaire *[jwa-ye(r)-za-nee-vair-sair]* Happy Birthday
Merci *[mair-see]* Thank you
Tu as quel âge? *[tew-a-kell-aj]* How old are you?
J'ai huit ans *[jay-weet-on(g)]* I am eight years old

QU'EST-CE QUE C'EST? *[kess-ke(r)-say]* WHAT IS IT?
une souris *[ewn-soo-ree]* a mouse
un poisson *[un(g)-pwa-son(g)]* a fish
un lapin *[un(g)-la-pan(g)]* a rabbit
un chat *[un(g)-sha]* a cat
un chien *[un(g)-shee-an(g)]* a dog
un oiseau *[un(g)-wa-zo]* a bird
j'ai *[jay]* I have
une tortue *[ewn-tor-tew]* a tortoise
et *[ay]* and

LES FRERES ET SOEURS *[lay-frair-ay-sir]* BROTHERS AND SISTERS
la famille d'Antoine *[la fa-meeye(r)-don(g)-twan]* Antoine's family
le grand-père *[gron(g)-pair]* grandfather
la grand-mère *[gron(g)-mair]* grandmother
mon père *[mon(g)-pair]* my father
ma mère *[ma-mair]* my mother
mon frère *[mon(g)-frair]* my brother
ma sœur *[ma-sir]* my sister
moi *[mwa]* me
Tu as des frères et des sœurs? *[tew-a-day-frair-ay-day-sir]* Do you have any brothers and sisters?
oui *[wee]* yes
j'ai un frère et une sœur *[jay-un(g)-frair-ay-ewn-sir]* I have a brother and a sister
non *[non(g)]* no
je suis enfant unique *[je(r)-swee-on(g)-fon(g)-ew-neek]* I am an only child
mais *[may]* but